shaping
the new
NHS

WHAT IS THE REAL COST OF MORE PATIENT CHOICE?

JOHN APPLEBY, ANTHONY HARRISON, NANCY DEVLIN

Published by:

A O4O7 31

King's Fund
11–13 Cavendish Square
London W1G 0AN
www.kingsfund.org.uk

© King's Fund 2003

Charity registration number: 207401   *W 65*

First published 2003

ISBN 185717 473 9

Available from:

King's Fund Bookshop
11–13 Cavendish Square
London W1G 0AN
Tel: 020 7307 2591
Fax: 020 7307 2801
www.kingsfund.org.uk/publications

Edited by Eleanor Stanley
Cover design by Minuche Mazumdar Farrar
Printed and bound in Great Britain

Contents

About the authors   v

Preface   vii

Introduction: improving patient choice   1

The current policy context for patient choice   5
Existing restrictions on choice   7
Pressures to extend choice   8
Summary   12

Promoting choice: the benefits and costs   14
The value of choice   14
What choices might patients exercise?   16
Summary   22

Constraints on patient choice   23
Individual versus collective choice   23
Knowledge and the ability to make informed choices   24
Economic factors   25
Implications for society   27
Safety and quality   28
Ethical concerns   29
Supply limitations   30
Conflicts with other objectives   32
Summary   35

The heart surgery choice scheme: a case study   37
Background   37
Aims   38
Eligibility   38

Funding   38
Impact   39
Other consequences   43
Summary   45

Conclusions   46
How far is choice limited in the NHS?   46
What kinds of choice are possible and desirable?   47
What are the benefits of choice?   47
What are the costs of improving patient choice?   48
Is choice a substitute for patient and public involvement?   49
What is effective choice?   49
Will current government efforts to promote choice
be successful?   50
Can the NHS offer greater choice within the existing
policy framework?   50

Ways forward   51

Endnotes   53

References   56

Linked publications   59

About the authors

John Appleby
Chief Economist at the King's Fund, and Visiting Professor at the department of economics at City University, London

John previously worked in the NHS and at the Universities of Birmingham and East Anglia as senior lecturer in health economics. He has published widely on many aspects of health service funding. His current work includes research into health care performance measures and rationing.

Anthony Harrison
Fellow in Health Systems at the King's Fund

Anthony worked in the Government Economic Service until 1981. He has published extensively on the future of hospital care in the UK, the private finance initiative and waiting list management and has recently published a study of publicly funded research and development.

Nancy Devlin
Professor of Health Economics at City University, and visiting Senior Fellow at the King's Fund, London

Before joining City University in 2002, Nancy was Fellow in Health Systems at the King's Fund and held senior lecturer posts in economics in New Zealand. She has published on a range of health economics topics, including health care system reforms, economic evaluation, production functions, health care spending, rationing, equity and the economics of dental care.

Preface

It is easy to characterise the NHS as a somewhat paternalistic institution where patients are expected to do as they are told, take what they are given and to be, if not grateful, then happy with their lot. But it is easy to forget that before the creation of the NHS, choice in health care was a luxury reserved for the well off. For those without the financial means, access to health care was extremely limited.

However, access to care is not the same as access to high-quality care, and the ability to choose to be treated is not the same thing as choosing how and where to be treated. While income may no longer be a barrier, public expectations of what the NHS should provide – and how quickly – have undoubtedly changed. As a result, then, improving choice has tremendous popular and political appeal: who could argue against the desirability of allowing patients more say in decisions concerning their health?

A new challenge for the NHS, therefore – indeed, for all public services – is not only how to expand the scale and scope of choice but what types of choices should be provided and, crucially, where choice conflicts with other desirable goals, what we are prepared to give up to improve choice.

The King's Fund discussion paper, *The Future of the NHS: A framework for debate* (King's Fund 2002a), suggested that while the health service could benefit from increased resources, it also needed to grapple with new ways of working and new relationships.

In particular, it suggested that ways should be investigated to create an arm's-length relationship between the NHS and central Government;

that consideration should be given to ensuring greater permanent local autonomy for NHS trusts – perhaps reconstituted as new, not-for-profit organisations – and that the NHS should examine how best to expand patient choice.

This new discussion paper forms part of a series of continuing policy analysis exploring emerging ideas and initiatives in health care, and concentrates on the proposal for expanding patient choice outlined in *The Future of the NHS*.

Other policy work from the King's Fund, linked to *The Future of the NHS*, is currently exploring the role of markets in health care; whether there is a role for an arm's-length agency, independent of the Department of Health, to run the NHS; and whether US-style managed care can offer lessons for the NHS on the management of chronic diseases.

Introduction: improving patient choice

Choice mechanisms enhance equity by exerting pressure on low-quality or incompetent providers. Competitive pressures and incentives drive up quality, efficiency and responsiveness in the public sector. Choice leads to higher standards.

The overriding principle is clear. We should give poorer patients... the same range of choices the rich have always enjoyed. In a heterogeneous society where there is enormous variation in needs and preferences, public services must be equipped to respond.

Tony Blair speaking at South Camden Community College, 23 January 2003 (Blair 2003)

Where the Government is committed to public services free at the point of use and available to all on the basis of need, it is important to ensure that choice is not promoted at the expense of equity or efficiency, particularly where there are market failures and capacity constraints.

Public services: meeting the productivity challenge (HM Treasury 2003)

The Prime Minister's message could hardly be clearer: public services such as the NHS have no choice but to offer choice. The Treasury, on the other hand, sounds a note of caution, pointing out that while choice may be desirable, it cannot be achieved without cost.

Of course, it is easy to overlook the fact that the NHS is the very embodiment of choice: its creation extended access to treatment and care to millions of people who had previously been unable to exercise this fundamental choice because of their lack of income.

However, access to care is not the same as access to high-quality care, and the ability to choose to be treated is not the same thing as choosing how and where to be treated. While income may no longer be a barrier, public expectations of what the NHS should provide – and how quickly – have become higher. Improving choice, therefore, has tremendous popular and political appeal: who could argue against the desirability of allowing patients more say in decisions concerning them? At first glance, improving choice seems unequivocally 'a good thing', and tentative policy steps in this direction – such as allowing people waiting six months for an operation to choose where to be treated (*see* The heart surgery choice scheme: a case study) – a good idea.

But what trade-offs are involved – and what price are we prepared to pay for more choice? If individual patients are not expected to bear the cost of the choices they make – as in a market – then who does? Are patients always willing and able to exercise choice in their own best interests? Are there limits to the choices that should be offered – either in the interests of individual patients or the population? Importantly, how far should we go in extending choice while still retaining the essential objectives of the NHS?

This discussion paper identifies the key issues that the Government must take into account if it wishes to make patient choice a guiding principle of the taxpayer-funded health care system. Two major constraints on the development of choice have to be recognised from the outset.

First, there is an irreconcilable conflict – in the context of a fixed health care budget – between allowing individual patients unconstrained choice of treatments that are free at the point of consumption, and the allocation of resources in a cost-effective manner. Individuals may choose treatments that are the most effective (and that best meet their preferences) but not the most cost-effective (or that reflect the preferences of society as a whole) – with corresponding opportunity costs in terms of health gain foregone by other patients. One patient's choice may deny another's treatment.

Second, the wider policy framework surrounding choice is, at present, poorly developed. For example, the equity issues associated with choice have not, at present, been considered: 'equity' was, notably, absent from the list of 'key principles' that local systems of patient choice needed to heed when implementing a number of choice pilot schemes proposed in the Department of Health discussion document, *Extending choice for patients* (DoH 2001a). If everyone is offered choice, does this resolve equity concerns? What if choices are more likely to be exercised by those who are more educated, more articulate, more able to travel? And while increased patient choice may exert pressure on poorly-performing providers to improve their services, there is no reason to think, despite the Prime Minister's assertion, that this will ensure the equal treatment of those in equal need. Hence, extending choice puts at risk a key objective of the NHS – equal access for equal need.

These considerations give rise to a series of questions addressed in this paper:

- How far is choice limited in the NHS?
- What kinds of choice are possible and desirable?
- What are the benefits of choice?
- What are the costs of improving patient choice?
- Is choice a substitute for patient and public involvement?
- What is effective choice?
- Will current government efforts to promote choice be successful?
- Can the NHS offer greater choice within the existing policy framework?

We argue that current initiatives in this area are motivated as much by the desire to reduce waiting times as by the objective of improving choice. Moving beyond these initiatives will require caution, as the benefits of extending choice are almost always at the expense of other benefits.

At the heart of this debate is the question of whether choice is a means to an end or an end in itself. If it is an end in itself, what value do we place on it and what we are prepared to sacrifice to obtain it?

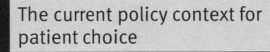

The current policy context for patient choice

In May 2002 Alan Milburn, Secretary of State for Health in England, gave a speech to the NHS Confederation Conference in which he announced that, in place of the monolithic, nationally-run service, a new NHS was to be developed 'in which there is greater plurality in local services with the freedom to innovate and respond to patient needs'. (Milburn 2002)

This was the Government's response to critics who argued that the current NHS could never provide the kind of service a choice-conscious public increasingly wants. The old health service was, at the time of its foundation, a world leader: now, Mr Milburn argued, it is seen as out of date, unfit for a world of informed users accustomed to choosing from an ever-wider range of goods and services. The United Kingdom had led the world in developing choice in what had once been publicly-run monopolies such as electricity and telephones: only the NHS remained to be radically reformed. Few other countries had adopted the NHS model; those that had instead set up decentralised and diverse systems of health care were now providing not only better services, but also greater choice and easier access for patients. The Government could provide extra resources and bring UK spending up to the levels of comparable countries, but this alone would be insufficient: the system itself had to be changed.

Although most NHS users are satisfied with the service they receive (Mulligan and Appleby 2001), surveys also show that many people think NHS services are inflexible and hard to access (*see* results from the NHS patients' survey programme: NHS 2003). These weaknesses could, of course, be the result of inadequate resources: if the NHS had more doctors and nurses and more modern equipment, it could match the performance of other countries. This was essentially the Government's view from its 1997 white paper (DoH 1997) through to the 2000 NHS Plan (SoS 2000) and its implementation programme (DoH 2001b).

In his 2002 speech, however, the Secretary of State now sided with his critics: while re-affirming the core concepts of the NHS – universal access based on need, not ability to pay – he argued that the supply side of the NHS had to be transformed, partly because it needed to provide its users with greater choice. He thus moved patient choice to the centre of the political stage – and in so doing gave the NHS a new objective.

Since Mr Milburn's speech, two major initiatives to extend patient choice have begun. First, patients waiting more than six months for heart surgery in England are now being offered quicker treatment elsewhere in the NHS, in the private sector or even abroad (DoH, 2002a). Secondly, in London, patients from selected specialities also waiting around six months have been offered a similar choice of quicker treatment. By June 2003, all patients in London waiting six months will be offered this choice.

These initiatives have also been partly responsible for changing the way money flows around the NHS. In April 2003, the 'payments by results' initiative (DoH 2002c) began its phased implementation: NHS trusts will now receive part of their income on the basis of a fixed cost per case – for specific treatments associated with long waiting times. This linking of patient choice with the movement of money around the NHS in effect creates a market for the services in question, which in theory should put pressure on high-cost providers to improve their performance. Thus, current policy on patient choice in the NHS is being largely driven by the goals of reducing waiting times and improving efficiency.

When announcing the new initiative, the Secretary of State did not explain how choice might be promoted across the whole of the NHS, nor did he say how this new objective fitted in with the other objectives of the NHS, such as equity of access for a given level of need. Similarly, he failed to explain how patient choice will fit in with the other initiatives and activities[1] aimed at aligning the type of services, and the way they are delivered, with the preferences of patients and users.

However, this is not to say that the scope for choice will not, or should not, be extended in other areas. As we shall see below, there are major pressures on the NHS to extend patient choice, and several initiatives to promote choice have already begun, some of them dating back to the previous administration. But first we should examine more closely the restrictions on user choice that currently operate within the NHS.

Existing restrictions on choice

For most of its existence, the NHS offered patients very little choice of where, when, how and by whom they were treated.[2] These restrictions were rarely questioned.

By the time the new health service was established as a national institution, the supply side of the health economy was already tightly controlled through the licensing of practitioners and of the dispensing of medicines. These controls were justified in terms of the interests of patients who could not be trusted to make sensible decisions about who should treat them and in what way. The NHS added a further and fundamental control: access to specialists. Emergencies apart, people could only seek specialist help following a referral from a general practitioner (GP).

But significant areas remained open to choice: GPs could, if they wished, refer their patients to any specialist; patients could choose their GPs (and GPs their patients); and those not wishing to use the NHS could choose private health care if they could afford it.

The components of the service on offer were not explicitly limited, and even where – as with child immunisation and vaccination programmes – there was strong implicit pressure to take part, there was, in contrast to some other countries, no compulsion or sanction. The NHS was diverse at the time of its foundation and has remained so, but that diversity arose from a lack of central control over the range of services and their quality. As a result, the energetic or well-informed GP might be able to offer a worthwhile choice to a patient needing specialist help: for example, a consultation with a London specialist rather than a local one. But this choice resulted from quirks in the system rather than its inherent characteristics – and it was not open to all.

In general, however, the restriction of user choice in key areas was and has been seen as a source of benefit. For example, the inability of patients to refer themselves directly to a specialist has been widely seen as advantageous, not least because it reduces inappropriate use of expensive resources such as consultants. Similarly, the use of triage in casualty departments has been justified on the grounds that it improves the efficiency of the service: the implicit trade-off is between efficiency and the patient's choice of health care practitioner (for example, a nurse rather than a doctor).

Pressures to extend choice

These restrictions were based on the assumption that professionals knew best how to treat a patient and that the ability of patients to treat themselves was limited by their lack of expertise. But these assumptions are no longer as acceptable as they were. For more than a decade, the NHS and other health care systems have been under pressure to make their services more responsive to users, and they have reacted by introducing a wide range of measures – including the extension of patient choice. Here we examine the chief social and economic pressures at work.

Consumerism

In 1991, partly in response to the growing demand for more responsive services, the Conservative Government attempted to create an internal NHS market – a reform which, combined with the introduction of GP fundholding, in principle offered patients a choice of where they could be treated. A Patient's Charter was introduced, which among other things strengthened the user's right to change GP. (In the event, these measures promised more than they delivered, and when Labour came to power in 1997, both the internal market and GP fundholding were quietly buried.)

In some cases, grass-roots pressure persuaded the Conservative administration to preserve existing options and to create new ones where choice had been eliminated. For example, the publication of *Changing Childbirth* (DoH 1993) demonstrated official acceptance of the principle that women should be allowed to choose their preferred method of delivery.

Elsewhere, well-organised and well-informed lobby groups – the majority focused on long-term conditions – campaigned for reforms in service provision. For example, the pressure to transfer the care of people with learning disabilities or mental health problems from large institutions to local facilities came partly from users and their representatives.

Wider availability of information

The power of professionals (not just in health care) has traditionally been based on exclusive access to information. Gradually, this source of power has been eroded. Even before use of the internet became widespread, there was a rapid growth in the availability of clinical information in the media, from voluntary agencies and the Government. In many areas, voluntary bodies became the centres of national expertise. It was eventually recognised that users might be able to command more information than professionals. This view found its fullest expression in the notion of the 'expert patient'.

The opportunity for people to become expert patients is particularly evident where they have to live with their illness for long periods of time. The longer lives, partly made possible by medical advances, have meant that the balance of ill health has shifted from acute to chronic conditions. People with chronic illnesses become familiar with their condition and are also more likely to take lifestyle and other factors into account. As a result – and again after pressure from user groups – the role of the 'expert patient' was acknowledged in the white paper *Saving Lives: Our healthier nation* (SoS 1999) and further developed in *The Expert Patient: A new approach to chronic disease management for the 21st century*, which states that today's patients can 'become key decision-makers in the treatment process' (DoH 2001b).

Self-care and the 'co-production' of health

Expert patients are capable not only of treating themselves but of determining what the treatment should be. The official promotion of self-care, however, was partly stimulated by economic factors. To the Conservative Government, increasing the range of over-the-counter medicines (OTCs) was a way of diverting demand away from the NHS. It also had the effect of restoring choice in areas where it had been eliminated.

Self-care implies that patients are the 'co-producers' of their own health, along with the health services: they have a set of choices, such as diet and lifestyle, which to some degree determine their health – and hence their need for health care. The white paper *Saving Lives: Our healthier nation* (SoS 1999) emphasised this notion of a partnership between individuals, the NHS and other organisations in promoting good health.

During the 1990s, the concept of 'patient partnership' (*see, for example*, NHS Executive 1996) emerged, reflecting the impact of consumerism and improved information on the relationship between doctors and other professionals, and those seeking care. Hence, it became established that patients should formally consent to treatment and also be offered information on the implications of different treatments (SoS 2000). Such measures partly transfer the exercise of choice from the professional to the patient.

Developments in clinical knowledge

In most parts of the economy, technological development has broadened the scope for choice by making available a wider range of goods and services. In health care, for example, new approaches have emerged and the range of OTC drugs has grown. Thus, for most conditions a wider variety of treatments are now available, each offering different chances of success.

But clinical developments have also begun to create choices that pose ethical dilemmas: for example, in the area of reproductive technology and genetics, or where technology has made it possible to sustain life indefinitely through continuous (and invariably expensive) medical intervention.

Here, consumerism has its limits: some choices have implications that go beyond the gratification of individual desires. Certain choices that are technically feasible, and for which people are prepared to pay, have therefore been made illegal.

Opting out

During the 1990s, the number of people covered by private medical insurance rose, largely through the growth of work-related schemes, but also because of an increase in self-payers.

The ability to pay-as-you-go and/or to purchase medical insurance is, however, only available to better-off people and those whose employers offer schemes. Among a much wider cross section of the population, another way of 'opting out' from the NHS has become popular: the use of complementary and alternative medicines (CAMs) (King's Fund 2002b).

Most of these services and products were unregulated, as it was assumed that they were unlikely to be harmful. During the 1990s, however, chiropractors and osteopaths came under statutory regulation – although not in a way that restricted growth in their numbers. Furthermore, their services, along with those of other alternative practitioners, gradually became available on the NHS. In the practices that offered these services, patients had a new set of choices (*see, for example*, King's Fund 2002b).

Summary

Recent policies for promoting patient choice focus solely on the option of quicker treatment for elective care. They stem from the Government's determination to explore every option for meeting the key NHS target of reducing waiting times for hospital treatment. In this context, patient choice not only exploits short-term spare capacity in the NHS and the private health care sector, but also exerts 'consumer' pressure on poorly-performing hospitals (which will see their workload and, importantly, their income reduce as patients choose other hospitals).

But many other forces are at work to increase demand for patient choice, such as the growth in consumerism, better information for patients and changing public attitudes towards health care professionals. Government policy has already started to respond to these demands.

But how far can choice be promoted in a cash-limited health service? Before attempting to answer this question, we need to examine:

- the benefits choice brings
- the range of potential choices available
- how the exercise of choice can be made effective
- when it seems appropriate to restrict individual choice in a collective health care system.

Promoting choice: the benefits and costs

There are many pressures on the NHS to widen patient choice. Yet choice sits uneasily in an institution whose funding, structure and objectives are determined by government on behalf of the nation.[3] Although this approach has obvious social benefits – such as equality of access for the whole population – tensions can also arise between what is good for society as a whole and what individuals feel is good for them personally. But the NHS is a personal service, and if there are demands for greater choice, how is the service to respond to these pressures, and what constraints on choice remain desirable? Here we look at what people value about choice and the range of possibilities for patient choice.

The value of choice

Why do people value choice? This is a case that scarcely needs to be argued, for choice defines the democratic capitalist state:[4] voters (through the ballot box) choose their politicians, and consumers (through their purchasing power) choose the goods and services they wish to buy. Similarly, individuals may, in most cases, choose whether or not to seek clinical advice – their ability to do so needs no justification.

But choice is also valued for the benefits it can bring. There are two main arguments here:

1. When people can take their money elsewhere, they put pressure on producers to be efficient and to develop new products.

If patients (or those acting for them) are able to choose between different providers, those not attracting users must respond by lowering prices or increasing quality – or go out of business. Moreover, if providers are themselves free to develop more effective services, then competition can provide a sustained impetus to improve care (provided, as we shall see below, certain conditions are met).

2. When people have a wide range of alternatives, they can choose the mixture of goods and services that best meets their preferences.

Choice is the necessary precondition for different wants to be satisfied, thus creating a better match between supply and demand. While choice in the first sense implies the existence of alternative providers of what might be very similar services, choice in this second sense implies diversity in the provision of care – offering either different ways of meeting the same need or the ability to respond to a diversity of needs.

In the United Kingdom and elsewhere, market processes have been introduced into the delivery of health care with the specific aim of promoting efficiency in service delivery; the reforms of the 1990s (*see* pp 8–12) were primarily justified on those grounds. However, the white paper proposing the reforms did not mention patient choice, although it did open the way for some patients to choose between waiting longer and being treated locally or travelling to distant hospitals for quicker treatment (*see, for example*, SoS 1989).

However, the market reforms did nothing to address the second argument for choice: diversity. The Patient's Charter and similar measures implicitly assumed that all NHS users wanted the same thing: shorter waiting times. But a large body of research – including social surveys and the testimony of CAM users – shows that preferences in health care delivery vary from individual to individual, according to a wide range of variables such as social circumstances, ethnicity and tolerance of drugs. Importantly, research also shows that while some people are distressed by delays in treatment, others are not (*see, for example*, Harrison and New 2000).

In summary, choice is valuable because:

- for a given need for care, people may choose different treatments based on their own assessment of the potential risks and benefits attached to those treatments
- for a given treatment, people may choose different delivery options: for example, home delivery of a child rather than hospital delivery
- for a given treatment and delivery option, people may choose different times of delivery: that is, they may trade off delay for other perceived benefits.

Next we look more closely at the types of choice that individuals might exercise.

What choices might patients exercise?

The state regulation and professional control that have characterised the NHS and other health care systems represent a strong presumption against unfettered user choice. However, the strength of this presumption varies according to the nature of the choices in question. Table 1 sets out the range of potential choices, which are then examined in turn.

TABLE 1: THE RANGE OF POTENTIAL CHOICES

CHOICE	COMMENT
Health-seeking behaviour	Choice of lifestyle, diet etc will have a fundamental impact on an individual's health – and hence need for health care.
Payer/purchaser Package of insured care	Choice of payer/purchaser or package of insured care within the NHS would require reorganisation of the system.
Whether to seek care or self-treat	A basic choice when ill is whether to seek professional care or to self-treat. Self-treating raises other issues concerning choice, eg access to drugs.
Type of care Treatment Health care professional Accepting advice	For type of care, it is usually possible to choose conventional or alternative medicine. Within both regimes there will be a range of treatment options provided by various practitioners, whose advice may or may not be accepted.
Provider Time of treatment	Choice of provider (public or private, local or not etc) and time of treatment are likely to be linked, although other factors (travel distance, quality of care offered etc) also inform choice.

Health-seeking behaviour

Most people have choices where their health-seeking behaviour is concerned, even though these may be limited by factors such as income and geography. The choices people make will influence their health status and hence their need for health care.

Health-seeking behaviour is usually left to individual choice, for the reasons given on p 16. But governments have also tried to influence this behaviour: for example, by promoting healthy eating and banning tobacco advertising. They have thus sought to bring individual choice into line with the collective interest without actually prohibiting choice (of course, legal restrictions apply to certain classes of drugs such as heroin, cocaine and cannabis).

Payer/purchaser and package of insured care

In a state system such as the NHS, the individual has little choice over the payer/purchaser and the package of care available. The separation of purchasers and providers by the 1991 reforms (SoS 1989) created some scope for choosing between treatment in different areas, and for intermediaries – such as health authorities and GP fundholders – to exercise choice on behalf of patients. Although it is hard to imagine someone choosing where to live on the basis of the local NHS purchaser, this choice theoretically exists even now.

A reorganised NHS could be envisaged in which exercising choice of payer/purchaser would be easier – but any choice resulting from a diversity of payers is likely to be severely limited.

During the 1990s, some health authorities attempted to define a health care 'package' – that is, what they would and would not pay for – but rarely got very far. This partly reflected the difficulty of taking away services people have got used to having, and partly reflected the strong pressures towards uniformity, for example, in the reaction to postcode rationing of drugs once differences between health authorities became known. Indeed, the more publicity that choices of this kind received, the greater the pressures for uniformity. For example, if the fact that CAMs are available in some areas and not in others becomes the subject of public debate, the expectation can only be that they will almost certainly be made available in all.

The present Government has added to the pressure towards uniformity by introducing national service frameworks and the National Institute for Clinical Excellence (NICE). These measures show a concern for equity: that everyone should have access to similar 'packages' of good-quality, well-provided services. Any major deviation from this objective in the name of choice is likely to be unacceptable.

Whether to seek care or self-treat

Perhaps the most basic choice is whether to seek health care or not, and if not, whether to self-treat. The choice of self-treatment is common, primarily for self-limiting conditions such as colds, headaches and minor injuries. The only exceptions are where people with certain mental health problems or a notifiable contagious disease are forcibly treated or constrained because they pose a danger to others.

In response to user demand and economic pressures, governments in recent years have extended the scope for self-care: for example, by broadening the range of OTC medicines, where the risks involved in allowing choice are assumed to be outweighed by the benefits. However, most health care systems still place some restrictions on the drugs and other forms of treatment available for self-care. Drawing the line between 'generally available' and 'not available' must be a collective decision; it would be unacceptable for a drug to be prescription-only in some parts of the country and not in others.

This conclusion, however, still rests on the view that users cannot be trusted to make decisions on their own and in their own best interests (*but see* p 10). An alternative view is that consumer sovereignty is appropriate in medicine – provided that users have the information they need and can obtain legal redress if misinformed. On this view, the regulation of drugs through, for example, the Medicines Control Agency is unnecessary since the legal framework applying to non-health goods and services would be sufficient to protect consumers of health care services. However, this assumes a much greater capacity to understand the implications of potentially dangerous choices than most patients possess. The debate about direct-to-consumer advertising (DTCA) of drugs centres on where the boundary should be drawn. The pharmaceutical industry claims that patients should be exposed to advertising, as it will give them the information they need to choose between drugs; but the opponents of DTCA claim that the information made available will be incomplete or unbalanced and thus lead to wrong choices.

The scope for self-treatment is likely to increase as more treatments are deregulated. But how far choice can be extended in this direction depends upon the public's acceptance of the risks involved. However, more investment in high-quality user information and in research designed to support self-care can reduce these risks.

Type of care and treatment options

Within the mainstream NHS, a choice of treatment exists for many conditions. The case for choice rests on the differences between users, in terms of how each treatment might affect them and what level of risk they will accept. The introduction of formal consent procedures and informed patient choice recognised this.

Complementary and alternative medicine (CAM) represents a more radical choice, as its practitioners often reject the very basis of orthodox medicine. As a generally unregulated area of medicine, CAM has offered choice to people dissatisfied with the NHS and/or conventional treatment, although they have had to pay for it themselves. Yet as we have seen (*see* p 12), CAM has recently infiltrated conventional medicine. So far this trend has not been challenged, perhaps because it has been experimental and modest in scale. But were the infiltration to go further, the question of clinical effectiveness and cost-effectiveness would arise; the evidence base for most complementary therapies is weak compared with that for most mainstream treatments. Again, it is a question of individual versus collective choice: people may want CAMs on the NHS – but should treatments of unknown efficacy be available 'free' and what would have to be foregone elsewhere to make them available?

Health care professional

The NHS was established around the medical profession, which largely determined what was 'legitimate' medical care. While treatment styles might differ, the choices available – between GPs, for example – were within a defined field of knowledge and type of expertise. People who wanted other styles of care would have to look outside the NHS.

Recently, however, users of the mainstream NHS have increasingly been able to seek care from nurses and other professionals directly, without a GP or doctor as intermediary. For example, the grass-roots pressure that led to the publication of *Changing Childbirth* (DoH 1993) reflected a desire among women to choose not only their method of delivery but also their main carer (midwife versus obstetrician). Moreover, recent extensions of prescribing rights to nurses and pharmacists open up new ways of accessing care not available hitherto.

Provider and treatment timing

Choice of provider is implicit in many of the above choices: between GPs, between GPs and other professions, between surgery sooner rather than later, and between mainstream and alternative medicine. Where hospitals are concerned, however, the choice has typically been between providers offering similar services: that is, elective operations.

In non-clinical matters, such as time of appointment and ease of access to treatment, the usual arguments for restricting choice do not apply. People can judge these matters for themselves and may well take different views: the access times or locations convenient for some will not be so for others. The choices people make will be influenced by their personal circumstances, such as how mobile they are and how much pain they are experiencing.

But patients are far less able to judge the quality of care in different locations. Although information about quality is slowly becoming available, informed choice is still difficult for lay people. It is theoretically possible to choose one's GP, but the shortage of GPs and the lack of information about their quality restrict this choice in practice.

The scope for exercising personal choice over when one would like to seek advice or be treated has, in practice, been very limited. This is partly because professionals have restricted access times, the treatments on offer and the way that services are supplied for reasons that often stem from self-interest: for example, surgery times may be limited to weekdays because surgery staff prefer it that way. Extending the scope for patient choice may be against the interests of those providing the service. Some of these access problems are being addressed through maximum waiting-time targets to see a primary health care professional.

Summary

Choice has potential benefits. Patients are better able to match their consumption of health care with their personal preferences; and pressure can be put on producers of health care to improve their performance.

But realising these benefits for users is fraught with problems. Patients are not always the best judges of their own welfare: the choices they make may not be the ones they might have made had they been better informed, for example. And realising the benefit of competitive pressure relies not just on the ability of patients to take their custom elsewhere, but also on the economic environment in which providers operate and how incentives to improve performance are structured.

But choice of provider is only one of a variety of possible choices patients could make in the NHS. The domain of choice extends from choices to self-treat, through to choice of 'purchasing agent', choice of treatment and its timing, and choices of health care professional. In each of these areas, choice has been limited whenever its costs are felt to outweigh potential benefits. However, the balance of costs and benefits can change over time: for example, in response to new health care technologies or shifts in public opinion.

Constraints on patient choice

Constraints on choice are not unique to 'non-market' health care systems. Even where markets have long existed, there have been restrictions on what health care is delivered and by whom. These reflect judgements about what choices are appropriate for consumers to make. The restrictions show national variations: for example, in some countries drugs that are restricted in the UK are freely available over the counter, and vice versa. Here we examine the arguments used to justify restrictions on user choice.

Individual versus collective choice

The case for offering choice in the areas described in Table 1 (p 16) rests on the presumption that individuals should be able to choose, unless there are compelling arguments against their doing so. But many health care decisions are collective rather than individual. Decisions about where to site hospitals, how big they are and what services they provide are made by the NHS on behalf of everyone who may use them. Similarly, decisions about whether a drug should be made available over the counter are made on behalf of all potential users.

This tension between what is 'good' collectively and what individuals would choose for themselves influences decisions on resource allocation in the NHS and health care generally. For example, to inform decisions about whether to provide new health care technologies or new treatments, clinical trials may seek evidence of the capacity of patients to benefit from these innovations. But this evidence is rarely clear-cut: individual responses to a health care intervention will vary. It may also be difficult to identify in advance which individuals are likely to benefit from the intervention.

These variations in the evidence from evaluations pose a problem for the people who decide upon resource allocation. Their usual solution is to calculate averages for health outcomes, satisfaction ratings and so on. This may help them to make broad decisions, but it does not guarantee that such decisions will not deny some people's opportunities for choice.[5]

The valuation of improved clinical outcomes also highlights potential tension between patients' views and collective views. While patients may be asked to indicate their satisfaction with care or, occasionally, their preparedness to pay (where a monetary value of the benefits they enjoy is sought), the valuations employed in the kind of economic evaluations routinely conducted in the NHS[6] are usually not those of patients, but of 'the general public'. Patients' values are seldom used, on the grounds that the views of the general public are more relevant as they are funding health care via taxes, and that general public valuations are less likely to be biased by self-interest. This identifies the fundamental question of what role patients' views and values should play in economic assessments and collective choices and, more generally, whose values determine health policy (*see* Devlin, Appleby *et al*, 2003). While choice emphasises the value of individual patients' views, in practice, as we shall see, collective or social values must inevitably override them.

Knowledge and the ability to make informed choices

In itself, exercising choice demands little prior knowledge – but informed choice does. For some of the areas of choice set out in Table 1, the information requirements are minimal. But others demand a great deal of information – in particular, the choice of treatment and provider.

The introduction of formal consent procedures means that patients must now be made aware of the risks involved in the choices facing them (*see, for example*, NHSE 2001).

However, the knowledge base upon which the NHS rests is patchy. The rise of evidence-based practice has revealed large areas of conventional medicine where there has been little or no research. The same applies, even more strongly, to CAMs – although individuals are free to use their own money on unproven treatments, it is hard to make a case for using public funds in this way.

Even if consumers are well informed about the quality of the services on offer, it does not follow that their choices will be in their own best interests. They may make a 'bad' choice for a variety of reasons: for example, inability to complete the necessary mental tasks; a 'weakness of will'; or emotional decision-making (*see* New 1999).

Furthermore, although the general trend in recent years has been to provide patients with more information about their treatment options, not everyone wishes to choose for themselves – particularly when the merits of the alternatives facing them are hard to assess. They may choose not to choose (*see* Schneider 1998).

Thus, the requirements for informed choice are demanding: not only for the individual, faced with a mass of hard-to-understand information, but also for the health care system, which has to provide that information.

Economic factors

All health care systems must limit user choice if they are to keep within budget. These financial constraints can apply at various levels:

Restricting the 'bundle' of services available

In contrast to insurance-based schemes, the NHS does not explicitly define all the services it will fund and provide. Through NICE, however, it has begun the process of 'bundle definition' at national level. Taxpayer-funded resources will be allocated so as to maximise total improvements in health (or to reduce inequalities in health). Given this, as Rudolf Klein has observed, 'The conclusion must therefore be that maximising individual patient choice is incompatible, given constrained budgets, with maximising the welfare of the patient population as a whole unless there were an open-ended financial commitment to health care. Short of that, patient sovereignty is likely to be an illusion.' (Klein 2002). This process/policy will inevitably restrict the areas in which choice may be exercised.

Eligibility criteria for health care providers

Through legislation, the imposition of quality standards and other means, the Government effectively limits the range of health care providers. But some countries impose further limits – for example, preferred providers – in order to control costs.

Natural monopoly and economies of scale and scope

Most health care activities are, by industrial standards, small in scale: the typical GP practice, like other community-based services, comprises a handful of professionals and support staff. This means that all but the smallest communities can support more than one provider of most community health services. But the same is not true of hospitals.

Hospital departments may also be small in terms of the number of professional staff they directly employ, but each department uses facilities that are both expensive and, in some cases, subject to economies of scale. For some hospital services, particularly acute emergency care, both economic and quality considerations require large catchment areas. For example, developments in cancer care have been based on the concept of large clinical networks, linking hospitals and community services over catchment areas of up to 2 million people. In such circumstances, choice of the provider of a particular form of treatment may not be possible for most people.

Recent developments have caused a reduction in the number of hospitals. The trend towards clinical specialisation has favoured the growth of larger institutions, while concerns over quality and risk have led to the demise of smaller local hospitals.

The evidence on economies of scale and scope in hospitals, though limited, does suggest that for many types of elective care the quality threshold is fairly low. Furthermore, as surgeons are mobile, they can carry out low-risk procedures away from large hospitals. This means that choice of location is feasible for a large proportion of the people needing elective care.

The evidence and the arguments are different for emergency care. At the 'lower' end of the scale – for example, minor-injuries units – economies of scale and scope are limited and therefore many access points can be provided. At the 'higher' end – for example, trauma centres – economies are possible, supporting the case for large units with catchment areas of 500,000 people or more; this means that, in all but the largest communities, no choice can be offered.

However, in March 2003 the Department of Health published a consultation paper, *Keeping the NHS local* (DoH 2003a), which identified ways that small hospitals can provide a wider range of services. Many of these are already in common use, but some are experimental – so until their safety and cost-effectiveness can be evaluated, the scope for preserving the local option will remain unclear.

Implications for society

Situations where the consumption or non-consumption of goods or services by an individual can have negative or positive consequences not only for the individual, but also for others in society, raise difficult questions about how far individual choice should be restricted in the interests of others. For example, the UK Government has generally allowed parents to opt out of programmes with significant societal implications, such as child immunisation and vaccination; but it has simultaneously sought to maintain vaccination rates by offering GPs a financial incentive to treat as many children as possible.

This appears to be a straightforward conflict between individual and collective interest, and the response will be primarily political. But the credibility of placing restrictions on choice depends upon the evidence available to support the collective decision: for example, during the recent controversies surrounding the combined MMR vaccine, the perception among parents of the risks of triple vaccination shows how patient choice can be influenced by 'evidence' that is disputed scientifically.

Safety and quality

Health care systems may also restrict choice in the interest of user safety: for example, by controlling access to drugs judged to be dangerous unless administered by professionals.

Since the 1968 Medicines Act, before drugs enter the marketplace, they are subject to a licensing procedure designed to assess their safety as well as their efficacy. Although specific aspects of this procedure are subject to criticism (Harrison 2003), in general it is hard to argue against some restriction of this sort, given the risks to health that the improper use of drugs can pose. But there are exceptions. First, in cases of serious illness where there are no effective treatments, patients may accept a degree of risk that the licensing procedure would regard as unacceptable.[7] Second, recent measures from the European Union to bring herbal medicines within a licensing framework have been criticised precisely on the grounds that they limit choice. The Government, however, denies this (DoH 2003b).

All health care systems operate some form of licensing for health care providers on safety and quality-assurance grounds. Critics of this form of regulation have tended to focus on the dangers of allowing professions to control entry to their own profession and to regulate themselves. Recent initiatives in the UK designed to protect patients reflect concerns raised by, for example, the tragedies at the Bristol Royal Infirmary and other untoward incidents. Again, at a general level, it is hard to argue against restrictions of this sort. Historically, however, professional self-regulation has been used to protect narrow professional interests in the name of patient safety. Recent government initiatives, as well as professional ones, have attacked many of these restrictions head-on. For example, the Health and Social Care Act 2002 allows for nurses and pharmacists to take over prescribing roles. More generally, the Government has made it clear that it wishes to seek greater flexibility of career paths and roles that, while promoting efficiency, make it easier to introduce choices where these involve changes in professional behaviour.

Ethical concerns

Individual choice may also be restricted if it is held to contravene widely held social values. For example, ethical concerns about IVF and donor insemination, as well as human stem-cell research and cloning, led to the setting up of the Human Fertilisation and Embryology Authority (HFEA).[8]

Similarly, restrictions may be imposed on individuals not considered competent to make choices about their health care: for example, those suffering from severe mental illness or cognitive disability. And, of course, children are barred from many health care choices – such as contraception and consent to treatment – open to adults.

The limits to individual choice in these areas will continue to be a matter for debate, partly because society's values are constantly evolving and partly because of advances in knowledge (both of which can help resolve previous ethical dilemmas as well as create new ones).

Supply limitations

In the short term, the scope for extending choice is limited by the availability of the required capacity. By 'availability', we mean reasonable access, adequate capacity and genuine responsiveness – that is, the ability to shift resources to new services in response to changes in patient choice. The health care labour market will need to show similar flexibility in the face of changing demands; and the commissioning process for medical research should be responsive to the wishes of the public and patients. We consider these themes in turn.

Genuine alternatives in provision

As we have seen, there may sometimes in theory be scope for creating alternative providers, but the costs may be prohibitive. In the case of emergency care, for example, the case for a single provider – or provider system – in most parts of the country (and outside the main conurbations) is strong. For other services, the cost penalties and hence the balance of advantage is less clear-cut.

Effective availability

The notion of effective availability takes into account restrictions on access (such as limited opening hours, or distance) that, while not posing absolute constraints on choice, may limit it to such an extent that in practice some groups have very little choice, or the choices offered to them impose high personal costs such as significant loss of earnings or long and expensive journeys.

Adequate capacity and responsiveness

Adequate capacity and responsiveness are essential if the NHS is to be able to re-allocate its resources in favour of the services or providers that people choose over others. But if extra capacity is not available to meet the new demand, those who gain from choice are doing so at the expense of someone else's health care needs.

Flexible health care labour markets

Many health care resources are specific to particular activities – and developing new resources takes time because of the long training periods typical of health care. New areas of choice that require rapid expansion in activity will only be possible if there is flexibility in labour markets. But, as with the current drive to increase elective care, a major barrier to expansion has been the historic restrictions on the supply of medical and nursing staff, and the associated demarcations between professional groups.

Responsive research

Responsiveness in health care research is particularly important for new services, including CAMs, where existing evidence is limited and traditional mechanisms – such as industry-financed programmes – are unlikely to be appropriate.

Generally speaking, however, unless those who plan, fund and carry out research into health care reflect the wishes of the public and patients – and the evidence is that they do not (Harrison 2002) – the choice of available treatments and delivery options will in future be limited.

Conflicts with other objectives

The pursuit of choice may put other health care objectives at risk. Here we look at three key objectives of the NHS: equity, efficiency and quality.

Equity

As noted in Chapter 1, current policy initiatives to improve choice focus on patient choice of provider, and aim to provide faster treatment for those waiting over six months. By utilising spare and additional capacity within the NHS and elsewhere, the heart surgery choice scheme and the London Patients' Choice project will serve to help even out variations in waiting times. To this extent (as has been noted by Alan Milburn – Milburn 2003) choice helps to reduce access inequalities. However, the implications for equity of extending patient choice depend upon the type of choice involved and how we view the concept of equity. So, although the Prime Minister has praised choice of provider as a means to 'enhance equity by exerting pressure on low quality or incompetent providers' (Blair 2003), there is no reason to think that it will necessarily ensure equity of delivery in terms of the equal treatment of people in equal need.

For example, if two patients with equal needs are offered the choice of faster treatment, and one accepts the offer while the other rejects it, is this an equitable situation? In one sense, it is clearly inequitable: one patient receives the speedier treatment resulting from unequal access to care and thus enjoys better health for longer. However, since both patients were offered the choice, does this resolve concerns about equity? It may do if one adopts a broader definition of 'equity': that is, where individuals make their own calculations about the advantages and disadvantages of their choices, taking into account a wider range of factors than simply whether they have equal access to care.

If we accept this, then even if choice of provider should lead paradoxically to wider disparities in access to care, it could still be true that, overall, patients would enjoy greater utility. This is because the possibility of choice increases the chances of satisfying every individual's personal preferences. It is an example of Rawls's 'difference principle', where greater inequality can be justified as long as the difference in expectation is to the advantage of the worst-off person in society (Appleby, Harrison *et al* 2003).[9]

We need to know why some patients turn down an offer of faster treatment. If, for example, those on higher incomes take up such offers more readily than other people – perhaps because they place higher value on their time (Propper 1990, 1994) – we need to ask whether it is acceptable that income should play a role in determining speed of access to care.[10]

As we have seen, patient choice can also exert competitive pressure on poorly performing hospitals. But although choice of provider may give an incentive to improve, this is not the same as closing inequitable gaps in service provision and quality. In fact, hospitals that lose patients to other establishments because of patient choice could face a spiral of financial decline. Such hospitals might then have difficulty in responding to the 'market signals' of patient choice, resulting in poorer services for those patients remaining with their 'home' hospital – and a consequent widening of inequality.

Efficiency

Where the health care budget is fixed, some conflict is inevitable between allowing patients unconstrained choice between treatments that are free at the point of consumption, and allocating resources in a cost-effective manner. Not surprisingly, people will choose treatments that they understand to be the most clinically effective – but these are not necessarily the most cost-effective.[11]

However, as with the issues raised concerning equity (*see* pp 32–33), a question arises here as to the definition of efficiency (or at least, whose or what perspective to take on the matter). From the perspective of the individual patient, it is hard to see how it could be considered an efficient use of scarce resources if they were restricted in their choice of treatment only to those considered cost-effective (from the point of view of society as a whole). This is especially the case where, for a particular patient, the clinical effectiveness may be negligible (or worse, positively unbeneficial) even if, for the average patient, the treatment were deemed cost-effective.

The problem of generating adequate information from clinical trials and economic evaluations to inform decisions in the NHS was raised earlier in discussion about NICE (*see* p 25). There are two (at least) difficulties when the choice or decision is to be made by an individual patient. The first is the establishment of the 'threshold' level of cost-effectiveness used to classify drugs, treatments and so on as cost-effective. How costly per improved health outcome does a treatment have to be before it is considered not to be good 'value for money' at a societal level?[12]

Secondly, it is often the case that the exact reactions (and health outcomes) of a particular patient to a treatment will be unknown prior to treatment. Hence, at the level of the individual patient, there will be situations where choice is being exercised without full information, and consequently a risk that choices made will lead to inefficient use of resources. Such uncertainties are also implicit, of course, in situations where health care professionals – not patients – make a choice of treatment. The practical issue here, however, concerns likely differences in the approach to decision-making between patients

and professionals, and differences in access to information on risks
and outcomes. Whether patients will be more inclined to take decisions
about treatment that lead to more inefficient use of resources than
health care professionals is an empirical issue on which there is only a
limited amount of evidence.

Quality

Although the Prime Minister has claimed that 'choice leads to higher
standards' (Blair 2003), there is no inevitable link between choice and
quality. For example, current initiatives to improve choice in the NHS are
to be linked with payment of a fixed tariff to hospitals (DoH 2002c); *see*
p 6. This will encourage the provision of greater volumes of care, but not
necessarily improvements in the quality or effectiveness of the care.[13]
In fact, greater choice may lead to reduced quality.

This means that, if patients are to make informed choices, they should
be told about the relative quality of different providers. In addition, we
may need well-policed national care standards to protect consumers.
The presumption in a national health service is that everyone should be
offered similar standards of care.

Summary

Choice is not a free good: its benefits must be weighed against its costs.
It may also conflict with other desirable values in health care. Because
of the costs of creating choice, different individuals and different
health care systems will have different views about the desirability of
its benefits.

Some decisions must be made collectively: for example, about the
licensing of drugs, the accreditation of staff and the location of
hospitals. Extending choice will also demand a workforce responsive

to the diversity of patients' wishes. The training and flexibility required could make this hard to achieve – particularly in the short to medium term.

But for as long as the supply side of health care remains dominated by professionals, responsiveness may be impossible. And if the supply side is not responsive, the value of choice will be determined by how the available resources are allocated. There is a risk that the benefits enjoyed by some will be at the expense of others.

For these reasons, there are bound to be limits placed upon individual choice. How restrictive these are will depend upon the nature of the choices involved, as not all choices have the same impact on other desirable objectives.

The heart surgery choice scheme: a case study

Background

The 2000 NHS Plan first indicated the Government's decision to improve patient choice in the NHS. While the Plan noted that the right of GPs to refer patients to the hospital of their (that is, the GP's) choice had been restored following the abolition of the internal market and the restrictions on extra-contractual referrals, it also proposed to strengthen patient choice. Specifically, the Plan stated that, 'Patients' choice over hospital treatment will be improved by ensuring that by 2005, every patient will be able to book every hospital appointment and elective admission, giving them a choice of a convenient date and time rather than being assigned a time by the hospital.'

The emphasis here was on the booking system and there were no other details as to how choice would be improved (and nothing on the consequences of increased choice – such as the need to redesign the method for paying hospitals).

A subsequent consultation document proposed a number of pilot schemes that would give long-wait patients the option of faster treatment at another hospital (DoH 2002a); a more detailed discussion document specifically about the heart surgery choice scheme was published in March 2002 (DoH 2002b). This scheme, along with the London Patients' Choice project, is currently subject to evaluation that is yet to be published. Here we describe how the heart surgery choice scheme was set up, and make some initial observations about its operation.

Aims

The scheme offers patients who have been waiting for heart surgery for more than six months the choice of faster treatment than they would otherwise obtain had they remained with their 'home' hospital. Departmental guidance (DoH 2002b) explains that the scheme is part of a general investment in additional capacity, which should ensure that, in five years' time, no heart surgery patients will have to wait unacceptably long periods for admission to hospital. The current scheme therefore seems to be a stopgap, opening up options for faster treatment in the short term before the planned expansion takes effect in the longer term.

Eligibility

The scheme covers England only and focuses on patients waiting six months or more for heart surgery, especially coronary heart bypass grafts (CABGs) and valve operations (percutaneous transluminal coronary angioplasty, or PCTAs) – procedures that account for around 90 per cent of cardiothoracic surgery. Prior to the scheme's introduction, just over 10,500 people were waiting for these operations, of whom just under 2,500 had been waiting for more than six months (see Table 2). The scheme targeted just under 1 per cent of the 250,000 patients of all types who had then been waiting for over six months.

An important principle underlying the heart surgery choice scheme has been that 'importing' hospitals should not offer shorter waits to patients from elsewhere than they currently offer to their 'home' patients.

Funding

Earmarked revenue funding of £100 million was set aside for 2002/03 to pay for the setting up of the scheme; employment of patient care advisers; the purchase of capacity (using a benchmark cost of

£9,000–£10,000 for CABGs and £4,000–£5,000 for PCTAs) and other initiatives and activities needed to meet the March 2003 target of a maximum wait of nine months. No figures are available yet on the actual costs of the scheme.

Impact

It is too early for a full assessment of the scheme's impact, as formal evaluation is still going on. However, we can observe the initial effect on waiting times and lists.

Take-up of faster treatment

Informal evidence made public in February 2003 (Milburn 2003) shows that, of the 5,000 or so patients waiting for over six months, (a cumulative total between July and December 2002 – hence larger than the figures in Table 2 covering two separate three-month periods), 3,500 were deemed clinically suitable for faster treatment and that, of these, around 1,700 took up the offer.

Why did more than half the patients turn the offer down? Some of them may no longer have needed or wanted an operation, but equally some may have wanted to stay with their 'home' hospital – perhaps because they had a good relationship with its nurses and consultants. Until we know whether there was any consistent difference between the personal characteristics (socio-economic group, education and so on) of those who accepted and those who rejected, we cannot draw any conclusions about the equity of the scheme.

Waiting lists and times

Official figures suggest that, in the second quarter of 2002/03, the number of patients waiting over six months for cardiothoracic surgery fell from around 3,000 to about 1,500 – well on course for meeting the NHS Plan targets (*see* Figure 1).

Although these reductions in waiting times seem encouraging, the available data covers only a short period at the beginning of the scheme. Moreover, without more sophisticated analysis, it is impossible to disentangle the impact of the scheme from that of other activities affecting waiting lists.

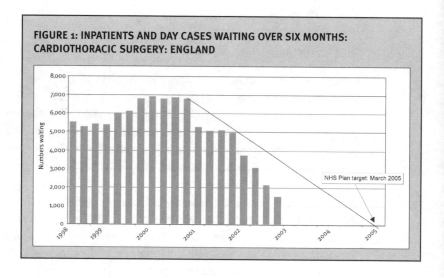

FIGURE 1: INPATIENTS AND DAY CASES WAITING OVER SIX MONTHS: CARDIOTHORACIC SURGERY: ENGLAND

Table 2 opposite shows the waiting-list and times situation for the specialty of cardiothoracic surgery for the first two quarters of 2002/03, broken down into the two main procedures constituting the choice scheme and all others making up the specialty.

While it is important to stress that these figures do not provide a complete picture of the waiting-times situation, only cover the first three months of the choice scheme, and cannot necessarily be wholly

TABLE 2: WAITING LIST AND TIMES FOR CARDIOTHORACIC SURGERY: ENGLAND: 1ST AND 2ND QUARTERS 2002/03

		TOTAL LIST	0–5 MONTHS	6+ MONTHS	9+ MONTHS
Cardiothoracic surgery: Total	1st Quarter	12,072	8,994	3,078	1,134
	2nd Quarter	10,778	8,616	2,162	570
	No. Change	−1,294	−378	−916	−564
	% Change	−10.7	−4.2	−29.8	−49.7
CABG	1st Quarter	7,095	5,045	2,050	728
	2nd Quarter	6,636	5,186	1,450	362
	No. Change	−459	141	−600	−366
	% Change	−6.5	2.8	−29.3	−50.3
PCTA	1st Quarter	3,414	2,968	446	102
	2nd Quarter	3,804	3,387	417	72
	No. Change	390	419	−29	−30
	% Change	11.4	14.1	−6.5	−29.4
CABG and PCTA	1st Quarter	10,509	8,013	2,496	830
	2nd Quarter	10,440	8,573	1,867	434
	No. Change	−69	560	−629	−396
	% Change	−0.7	7.0	−25.2	−47.7
Other procedures	1st Quarter	1,563	981	582	304
	2nd Quarter	338	43	295	136
	No. Change	−1225	−938	−287	−168
	% Change	−78.4	−95.6	−49.3	−55.3

attributed to the scheme, there are some tentative observations that can be made.

Although the combined list of CABG and PCTA patients waiting six months or more fell by a quarter, this was nearly matched by a rise in the numbers waiting between 0–5 months, leaving the overall waiting list for these procedures virtually unchanged. One interpretation of this 'bunching' effect is that it reflects a change in admission priorities towards patients waiting over six months and little, if any, increase in total activity. In the absence of the number of admissions to the waiting list, this interpretation remains speculative (it could be the case, for example, that activity has increased but also that admissions onto the list have risen, hence leading to a rise in the numbers waiting 0–5 months).

While the combined CABG and PCTA waiting list has remained unchanged, the list for CABGs has fallen, as has the number of patients waiting over six months. The number of CABG patients waiting 0–5 months has risen, but by much less than the fall in those waiting over six months. This would appear to suggest that the reduction in long waiters has been achieved mainly through additional activity (and/or a combination of increased activity and a reduction in the numbers admitted to the list).

On the other hand, the change in numbers of patients waiting for PCTAs reveals a very different pattern. As Table 2 shows, there was a small reduction in the number of patients waiting over six months, a large rise in those waiting 0–5 months and, consequently, a rise in the total PCTA list of 11.4 per cent.

It might be assumed that in concentrating on CABGs and PCTAs, patients with other needs may be neglected. In fact, there appears to have been a large fall not only in the total numbers waiting for other procedures within cardiothoracic surgery, but also in the numbers waiting 0–5 and over six months.

Overall, there appears to be some encouraging changes in waiting times in cardiothoracic surgery – although a somewhat mixed and yet to be fully explained picture within the specialty itself. However, the data is incomplete and only covers a short period at the beginning of the choice scheme. Moreover, without further more sophisticated analysis, it is impossible to disentangle the impact of the scheme from other simultaneous initiatives and activities bearing on waiting lists and times.

Other consequences

The attitudes of clinicians

Apart from the prime objective of reducing waiting times, two other consequences of the choice scheme are worth noting for their impact on service design, working practices and attitudes. The first concerns the attitudes and behaviour of clinicians – primarily cardiothoracic surgeons themselves, but also GPs in their referring roles.

The scheme greatly reduces the control specialists have historically had over their workload. It has achieved, in effect, a national pooling of waiting lists, with patients, through the sum of their individual decisions, acquiring much more influence over admission priorities. Furthermore, patient choice is bringing consultants very close to the 'market action': losing patients to another hospital and another consultant provides a powerful incentive to decrease waiting times. How consultants respond to these new circumstances will need to be evaluated.

If, as seems likely, choice of provider genuinely reduces waiting lists, GPs might respond by lowering the threshold for referral, leading to more referrals and a larger workload for hospitals. Hospitals may then retaliate by introducing demand management.

Patient care advisers

The task of offering patients a choice of faster treatment is carried out by the scheme's Patient care advisers (PCAs), who are usually nurses. The patients have, it seems, greatly appreciated the way the PCAs have done their job – not only because they helped them through the process of choice, but also because they are knowledgeable people who know the system and can provide information and support. This suggests that many patients feel rather neglected – if not completely forgotten about – until they arrive on the operating table.

The intervention of the PCAs may also lead to a more thorough validation of waiting lists. One explanation for the relatively low take-up of offers of faster treatment could be that many patients either did not need, or want, their operation.

The selection criteria for offering choice

The scheme has used a six-month wait as the criterion for offering choice, but this could pose problems of equity. It is quite possible that a person waiting six months for cardiothoracic surgery in one place may have different clinical characteristics from someone waiting six months somewhere else for the same operation. This is because:

- there are wide variations between trusts in terms of waiting lists and waiting times
- prioritising patients for surgery is largely done on the basis of waiting time (rather than their ability to benefit from surgery)
- elective surgery may be receiving different levels of resources between trusts, and be carried out with varying efficiency.

Waiting-time targets ensure equal treatment for equal waits, but do not guarantee equal treatment for equal need.[14] Thus, using the six-month criterion to select the patients to be offered choice may similarly fail to ensure equity in access to quicker treatment.

Summary

The main objective, at least in the short term, of the heart surgery choice scheme has been to reduce waiting times – specifically the numbers of patients waiting over six months. And, overall, there appears to be some encouraging changes in waiting times in cardiothoracic surgery – although a somewhat mixed and yet to be fully explained picture within the specialty itself. However, the data are incomplete and only cover a short period at the beginning of the choice scheme. Moreover, without further more sophisticated analysis, it is impossible to disentangle the impact of the scheme from other simultaneous initiatives and activities bearing on waiting lists and times.

As with any policy, it is not just important to evaluate service changes with respect to the policy's primary goals; there are always unintended consequences and knock-on effects – some good, some bad. While evidence of such effects remain either anecdotal or speculative, the heart surgery choice scheme's Patient care advisers appear to be popular with patients. The impact the scheme will have on the behaviour of consultants and GPs remains speculative. However, the scheme could play an important part in changing the way waiting lists are managed, the referral behaviour of GPs, and the attitudes and behaviour of consultants.

Conclusions

At the start of this discussion paper we asked eight questions raised by recent moves to extend patient choice. Here we revisit those questions and propose some answers.

How far is choice limited in the NHS?

It is important to note that all health care systems restrict choice in various ways – limiting patients' choice is not the exclusive domain of the NHS. For example, health maintenance organisations in the United States restrict enrolees' choice of provider purely on the grounds of financial viability. All health systems have certain restrictions on choice in common, including regulations on who can (and cannot) practise medicine; what drugs can (and cannot) be purchased without a prescription; and what drugs can (and cannot) be made available for use, whether by prescription or direct purchase.

In addition, all systems restrict choices that are agreed to be unethical (such as human cloning), where the public interest outweighs the individual's right to choose (such as mental health sectioning), or where individuals are deemed incompetent to exercise informed choice (such as due to cognitive impairment).

In each case, these restrictions reflect the belief that consumers are not always well enough informed to make health care decisions in their own best interests. The potentially serious consequences of a 'bad' decision are seen as justifying these restrictions. Each health care system may set these limits differently, but all of them have such limits.

What kinds of choice are possible and desirable?

Current policy has focused on the choice of secondary care provider, and has used waiting time as the sole criterion. However, the range of choices within the NHS is potentially far wider, and could include:

- personal health-seeking behaviour
- payer/purchaser
- package of care
- self-treatment
- type of treatment
- type of health care professional
- whether to accept professional advice
- provider
- time of treatment.

Each of these areas raises different issues when it comes to considering the limits to choice, the trade-offs between choice and key NHS objectives, and the benefits and costs of choice.

What are the benefits of choice?

The most obvious benefit of unrestricted choice is that individuals, if well informed, can select the services that are best for them, rather than being limited to the 'one size fits all' health care associated, perhaps unfairly, with nationalised health systems. What individuals choose as 'best' will be determined by how they value their own health; what risks they are prepared to accept; their genetic and physiological characteristics; what services they prefer; and how they want them delivered. A wholehearted commitment to extending choice would involve offering a range of different services, not just a choice between different suppliers of the same service.

Another benefit of choice is the competitive discipline it brings to bear on health care providers: if the money follows the patient, patient choice will encourage providers to provide high-quality services in an efficient manner.

What are the costs of improving patient choice?

None of the above benefits are guaranteed, nor do they arise *solely* from the presence of choice, nor are they without cost – either financial or in terms of other benefits that must be forgone.

Improving patient choice will require flexible capacity in the NHS. This may come partly from more efficient ways of providing services, but most types of choice will almost certainly create a need for additional resources.

Individual choice may also conflict with the choices available to others. For example, where there is a fixed health care budget, allowing people to choose treatments that are not cost-effective – although they may be clinically effective for that person – may limit the choice open to others.

Effective choice (*see* opposite) also relies on the availability of accurate information, not just for patients but for the professionals who help them to make the choices. No health care systems are yet generating the type of information needed to support patient choice adequately.

There may be less tangible costs too. Putting choice at the heart of the NHS can conflict with other NHS objectives if it leads to certain groups of people obtaining an advantage over others – this may be true of offering a choice of provider of the same service. But where choice leads to a greater variety of provision, it is unlikely to conflict with other NHS objectives.

Is choice a substitute for patient and public involvement?

Involving patients and the public in decisions about health care – through, for example, citizens' juries, NICE's Citizens' Council and consultations over anything from national policy to local services – can partly be seen as a substitute for patient choice, in that it provides patients with a 'voice' to ask for the services they want. But patient choice is not always a substitute for patient involvement. However far choice is extended to individuals, other forms of public involvement will be needed, since many choices – for example, on drug availability or service re-design – must be made collectively.

What is effective choice?

The key requirement here is flexibility in the provision of care, so that new types of service can be introduced. If provision cannot respond to the exercise of choice, then offering further choice will be pointless. Better information about the available options and their relative merits is also required.

Some shortfalls can be remedied relatively quickly, but others reflect a lack of research into areas of interest to patients.

Effective choice is more than simply knowing which hospital has the shortest waiting time. Before patients arrive at what they feel is an informed choice, they will increasingly want to assess other aspects of performance: most notably, quality of care and outcome of treatment. Currently, the NHS provides little or no information about quality that patients can use.

Will current government efforts to promote choice be successful?

The Government's recently introduced choice scheme for elective care will shorten the waiting time for people who would otherwise have to wait for six months or more. This will mean that others will have to wait longer, but even so, the scheme may be worthwhile. However, its main effect will be to put pressure on providers rather than to extend choice.

The two pilot schemes running since 2002 seem to be enabling certain patients to be treated more quickly than otherwise, but the evaluations are still under way. Not until we know the costs of achieving reductions in waiting times, and whether there were other unintended consequences (good and bad), will we be able to pronounce upon the success or failure of the schemes.

Can the NHS offer greater choice within the existing policy framework?

Even in its present form, the NHS has the potential to offer patients much greater choice than it currently does. However, the main message of this discussion paper is that, before this happens, we need a much more wide-ranging debate about how far patient choice should be extended, and what constraints are needed to prevent it from obstructing other desirable goals for the NHS.

Ways forward

Expansion of the scale and scope of choices open to NHS patients is one of a range of important, inter-linked issues shaping the future of our health service that need further research and analysis if decisions are to be based on sound evidence. The King's Fund will continue to contribute to wider debate, through research and publishing activities, and by hosting a series of expert debates. Our Shaping the New NHS programme will explore a number of key strands:

- The impact of new ways of reimbursing hospitals. Forms of competition and choice. We will research the expected (and unexpected) consequences of the new fixed-price market in the NHS, looking at the implications and likely results of the new system for paying hospitals being phased in this year.
- In collaboration with a number of other organisations and academics, we will contribute to an evaluation of the London Patients' Choice project.
- Choice and equity. We will explore how best to balance the interests of the individual consumer and the public as a whole in efforts to improve the quality of patient care, hosting an expert seminar in September 2003 and publicising the results.
- The role of market forces in primary care. We will examine whether stronger market incentives should be applied in primary care providers and primary care trusts – and, if so, how.
- The role of an 'arms-length' NHS agency. We will look at the case for and against continued direct management of the NHS by the Department of Health, and the feasibility of a new semi-independent health service.

- The role of medical professionalism. We will research how professionals might best be supported in order to respond to new challenges, such as stronger market incentives.
- The management of chronic care. We will research how stronger market forces might best be applied to enhance the management of patients with multiple and chronic medical conditions, drawing on lessons learned from managed care organisations in the United States.
- Decentralisation and the 'new localism'. We will analyse whether attempts by Government to decentralise power in the NHS, and to give the public more power in shaping health services locally, will improve provider responsiveness in ways that obviate the need for stronger market incentives.
- The role of information in health and health care. We are exploring the role and impact of increasing information in health and health care, through a series of workshops with users and providers of health services.

See Linked publications: forthcoming titles (pp 59–64) for details of proposed published outputs and dates.

Endnotes

1 For example, there are numerous initiatives designed to involve patients and the public in NHS decision-making, with the main objective of better ensuring that NHS services are more responsive to the needs of patients and carers. Such activities can, in some sense, be viewed as substitutes for direct choice exercised by individuals, and a step forward from the traditional principal-agent relationship whereby the NHS (such as politicians, primary care trusts, managers doctors and so on – the 'agents') make choices on behalf of patients (the 'principals').

2 However, it should be noted that, while limited, up to 1991 (and the introduction of extra-contractual referrals – ECRs), patients could request a referral to any consultant who would take them – statistics on the net inflow/outflow between the old regions of such 'cross boundary' flows of patients were collated at the end of the year and allocations to regions subsequently adjusted upwards or downwards. From 1997, 'out of area treatments' (OATs) replaced ECRs, and patients were discouraged from seeking care from providers that did not hold contracts with patients' 'home' purchasers.

3 It is not only the NHS as a collective system of health care provision that tends to limit choice. The way professional clinical and other groups have evolved (in the case of medicine, over centuries) has also, in some respects, served to trade off patient choice with professional self-interest to some degree.

4 Le Grand (2002) notes that under a liberal viewpoint, choice is desirable 'as an end in itself', regardless of whether the exercise of that choice has the consequence of improving welfare. He concludes that, both from a welfarist and the liberal perspective, the patient (not the doctor) should be sovereign, but he does not consider in any detail what the limits to that sovereignty might be.

5 Tensions between individual and collective choices are, of course, by
no means unique to the NHS or health care. All markets, for a variety of
reasons, trade off these aspects of choice. This issue is not a question of
absolutes but rather the degree of trade-off and where the line is drawn
between collective and individual benefit.

6 For example, the 'utility' weights applied to life years gained in the
calculation of quality adjusted life years (QALYs), the principal measure
of benefit used by NICE in its assessment of cost-effectiveness.

7 Last year, for example, a young British woman chose a new untried,
untested and unproven treatment for Creutzfeldt-Jakob Disease (CJD).
She was treated in the United States with a combination of quinacrine
and chlorpromazine and reportedly showed significant improvement.

8 The HFEA's main roles are to inspect clinics offering *in vitro*
fertilisation or donor insemination, or storing eggs, sperm or embryos,
to ensure they conform to high medical and professional standards. The
Authority also licenses and inspects research establishments engaged
in the field of human fertilisation, and provides a general information
resource for the public and health care professionals.

9 It is debatable, perhaps, whether a patient who turns down the offer
of faster treatment enjoys any greater benefit than if no choice were
offered, while those who take up the offer clearly do enjoy greater
benefits.

10 In fact, in a speech to NHS chief executives in February 2003, Alan
Milburn appeared to condone this inequality as it would serve to
preserve the NHS: 'The trap we must avoid is that identified by Richard
Titmuss four decades ago, of middle-class people opting out so that
public services become only for the poor and then end up being poor
services.' (Milburn 2003)

11 This also gives rise to an equity issue, as a choice that ignores the
cost-effectiveness of a treatment will result in corresponding opportunity
costs in terms of health gain foregone by other patients. One patient's
choice will deny another's treatment.

12 This is an important issue for NICE – *see* Towse *et al* 2002.

13 However, the incentive to increase volumes of care will depend on individual hospitals' costs vis a vis the tariff.

14 As an example of this, as part of its investigation into inpatient and outpatient waiting in the NHS in 2001 (NAO 2001), the National Audit Office carried out a survey in which nearly 300 (54 per cent) out of a sample of 558 consultants in three specialties considered that '...working to meet NHS waiting-list targets meant that they had to treat patients in a different order in 1999/2000 than their clinical priority indicated'. Of the 300 consultants, 20 per cent stated that treatment of patients in a different order had occurred frequently, and 80 per cent stated that deferring treatment of 'urgent' patients had had a negative impact on patients' health. It would appear from the NAO survey that urgent cases were displaced by less urgent patients in danger of breaching the (then) 18-month waiting-times target.

References

Appleby J, Harrison A, Dewar S (2003). 'Patients choosing their hospital: may not be fair and equitable'. *BMJ*, vol 326, pp 407–8.

Blair T (2003). *We must not waste this precious period of power*. Speech given at South Camden Community College, 23 January 2003. Available at: www.labour.org.uk/tbsocialjustice/

Department of Health (1993). *Changing Childbirth. Report of the Expert Maternity Group*. London: The Stationery Office.

Department of Health (1997). *The New NHS: modern, dependable*. London: The Stationery Office

Department of Health (2001a). *Extending Choice for Patients: A discussion document*. Proposals for pilot schemes to improve choice and provide faster treatment. London: Department of Health.

Department of Health (2001b). *The Expert Patient: A new approach to chronic disease management for the 21st century*. London: Department of Health.

Department of Health (2002a). *Start of patient choice is next step in delivering patient driven NHS*. Press release: 2002/0291.

Department of Health (2002b). *Extending choice for patients: Information and advice on establishing the heart surgery scheme: Draft for stakeholder consultation*. London: Department of Health.

Department of Health (2002c). *Reforming NHS Financial Flows: Introducing payment by results*. London: Department of Health.

Department of Health (2003a). *Keeping the NHS Local: A new direction of travel*. London: Department of Health.

Department of Health (2003b). *New legislation will stop second-rate products being sold: new herbal directive will protect consumers*. Press release: 2003/0023.

Devlin N, Appleby J, Parkin D (2003). 'Patients' views on explicit rationing: what are the implications for health service decision-making?'. *Journal of Health Services Research and Policy* (forthcoming).

Harrison A (2002). *Public Interest, Private Decisions: Health-related research in the UK*. London: King's Fund.

Harrison A (2003). *Public-Private Partnerships: The case for pharmaceuticals*. London: King's Fund (forthcoming)

Harrison A, New B (2000). *Access to Elective Care: What should really be done about waiting lists*. London: King's Fund.

HM Treasury (2003). *Public services: meeting the productivity challenge. A discussion document*. London: HM Treasury.

King's Fund (2002a) *The Future of the NHS: A framework for debate*. London: King's Fund.

King's Fund (2002b) *Level of NHS-funded Complementary and Alternative Medicines increasing, says the King's Fund*. Press release: 4 March 2002. London: King's Fund.

Klein R (2002). *'From pawn to queen': a commentary*. Unpublished paper presented at a meeting of the Health Equity Network

Le Grand, J (2002). *From pawn to queen. Economics, ethics and health policy*. Unpublished paper presented at a meeting of the Health Equity Network.

Milburn A (2002). *Diversity and choice within the NHS*. Speech to NHS Confederation annual conference, 24 May 2002.

Milburn A (2003). *Choice for all*. Speech to NHS Chief Executives, 11 February 2003. Available at: www.doh.gov.uk/speeches/milburnfeb03choice.htm

Mulligan J-A, Appleby J (2001). 'The NHS and Labour's battle for public opinion' in *British Social Attitudes: Public policy, social ties*, Park A, Curtice J, Thomson K, Jarvis L, Bromley C eds. The 18th report. London: Sage.

National Audit Office (2001). *Inpatient and Outpatient Waiting in the NHS.* HC 221, Parliamentary Session 2001–02. London: The Stationery Office.

National Health Service (2003). NHS patients' survey home page: www.doh.gov.uk/nhspatients/

New B (1999). 'Paternalism and public policy'. *Economics and Philosophy*, vol 15, pp 3–83.

NHS Executive (1996). *Annual Report 1995/1996. See* Section on patient partnerships at: www.doh.gov.uk/nhs95_96/pati.htm.

NHS Executive (2001). *Good practice in consent.* HSC 2001/023. London: NHS Executive.

Propper C (1990). 'Contingent valuation of time spent on NHS waiting lists'. *Economic Journal*, vol 100, pp 193–9.

Propper C (1994). 'The disutility of time spent on the UK's NHS waiting lists'. *Journal of Human Resources*, vol 30, pp 677–700.

Schneider CE (1998). *The Practice of Anatomy.* Cambridge University Press.

Secretaries of State for Health (1989). *Working for Patients.* Cm 555. London: The Stationery Office.

Secretaries of State for Health (1999). *Saving Lives: Our healthier nation.* Cm 4386. London: The Stationery Office.

Secretaries of State for Health (2000). *The NHS Plan.* Cmd 4818–I. London: The Stationery Office.

Towse A, Pritchard C, Devlin N (2002). *Cost-Effectiveness Thresholds: Economic and ethical issues.* London: King's Fund/Office for Health Economics.

Linked publications

We publish a wide range of titles about the NHS. See below for a selection of published and forthcoming titles. For the full range of current titles, visit our online bookshop at www.kingsfund.org.uk/publications or call our bookshop on 020 7307 2591.

PUBLISHED TITLES

Future Directions for Primary Care Trusts
Jennifer Dixon, Stephen Gillam, Richard Lewis

Primary care trusts (PCTs) are at the sharp end of the Government's hopes for a modernised NHS that is more responsive to patients and built on new models of social ownership. This web paper analyses their new role and asks how they might develop in the future. It constructs three possible scenarios for debate: one that puts the consumer in the driving seat and makes maximum use of competition; another that puts equity first and makes minimal use of market forces; and an 'ethical market' that uses competition selectively where it is consistent with PCTs' wider social mission.

8 May 2003 Free
Download at: www.kingsfund.org.uk/publications

Can Market Forces be Used for Good?
Jennifer Dixon, Julian Le Grand and Peter Smith

This discussion paper aims to open up an informed, transparent debate on how market forces may impact on the shape of the new NHS. It brings together the views of three seasoned commentators on the issue of market forces in the NHS: Julian Le Grand supports the introduction of stronger market incentives to prompt improved performance among secondary care providers; Peter Smith argues against even modest experimentation with stronger market incentives; while Jennifer Dixon asks whether it is possible to combine the best of market disciplines with planned provision.

ISBN 185717 477 1 19 May 2003 50pp £6.50

Sustaining Reductions in Waiting Times: Identifying successful strategies
John Appleby et al

Some trusts have been consistently successful in achieving – and in some cases, exceeding – the Government's inpatient waiting-time target of under six months. This web paper identifies the critical factors that have led to their success and analyses the context, including managerial and operational characteristics that might be transferable to other organisations.

May 2003 52pp Free
Download at: www.kingsfund.org.uk/publications

Claiming The Health Dividend: Unlocking the benefits of NHS spending
Anna Cooteed

The NHS is more than a provider of health services – it is the largest single organisation in the UK. How it recruits staff, procures food or constructs buildings affects the wider social, economic and environmental fabric of which it is part – which in turn affects people's health. This major report opens up an important debate about how the NHS might put its corporate muscle and spending power to work for health improvement and sustainable development – and in doing so ensure it promotes health, as well as offering health care.

ISBN 185717 464 X May 2002 150pp £10.00
Download a free report summary at www.kingsfund.org.uk/summaries

Five-Year Health Check: A review of government health policy 1997–2002
Anna Coote and John Appleby (eds)

When the Labour Government came to power in May 1997, it promised to 'save the NHS' by cutting waiting lists, improving service quality, raising spending and reducing health inequalities. Five years on, this comprehensive report scrutinises progress against pledges made by the Government during its first term of office in areas such as funding, staffing and quality of care. It argues that money alone, while crucial, will not build a new NHS, and that professional, motivated staff and a focus on wider health issues also have a key role to play.

ISBN 185717 463 1 April 2002 138pp £7.99

The Future of the NHS: A framework for debate

Should the Government be responsible for every 'dropped bedpan', or is it time for a decisive separation of political and managerial responsibilities? How can local responsiveness and innovation be supported alongside the drive for national standards? And can the extension of patient choice lever up quality? This paper, which brings together ideas from a group of commentators, academics and practitioners from health care and beyond, chaired by Lord Haskins, aims to stimulate the wider debate on which a reasoned, pragmatic consensus for the future depends.

Jan 2002 30pp Free
Download at: www.kingsfund.org.uk/publications

What Has New Labour Done for Primary Care? A balance sheet
Edited by Stephen Gillam. Foreword by Rudolf Klein

New Labour's first term in office saw a proliferation of new initiatives for the NHS. In primary care, these included significant changes in the form of the NHS Direct and walk-in health centres. This publication analyses the actual and potential impacts of these developments, and seeks to put them into the wider context of other changes in the NHS.

ISBN 185717 445 3 2001 128pp £7.99

The NHS – Facing the Future
Anthony Harrison and Jennifer Dixon

The NHS is under more pressure than ever before – from the public, the politicians and the media. This publication offers a wide-ranging examination of the modern health service, including new technology, an ageing population and rising consumer expectations. It argues that if the NHS is to survive in this new, more demanding environment, then standing still is not an option.

ISBN 185717 219 1 2000 342pp £17.99

The Politics of NHS Reform 1988–97: Metaphor or reality?
Chris Ham

How do the politicians closely involved with health and health care see the drive to reform the NHS that characterised the 1990s? Based on interviews with health secretaries who served between 1988–1997 – Kenneth Clarke, William Waldegrave, Virginia Bottomley and Stephen Dorrell – this publication probes their role and perceptions of what constituted a major experiment with internal markets.

ISBN 185717 417 8 2000 78pp £14.99

From Cradle to Grave
Geoffrey Rivett

Published to mark the NHS's 50th anniversary, this publication tells the extraordinary story of the health service. It gives a comprehensive overview of all the main landmarks, tracing achievements and breakthroughs in medicine, nursing, hospital development, and primary health care, in a way that combines both a clinical and a health management perspective.

ISBN 185717 148 9 1998 528pp £12.50

FORTHCOMING TITLES

SHAPING THE NEW NHS SERIES

Please note: titles and dates provisional at time of publication.

Is there a Role for an 'Arm's-length' NHS Agency?

Many people feel that politicians are still too involved in the day-to-day working of the NHS. This paper launches an important debate about whether the health service should continue to be directly managed by the Department of Health, and asks whether an 'arm's length' body with a semi-independent status similar to the BBC might be able to create more space for public, patients and professionals to improve health care.

ISBN 185717 474 7 2003 £6.50
Free download at: www.kingsfund.org.uk/publications

What Future for Medical Professionalism?

Recent debates such as the proposed changes to GPs' and consultants' contracts have raised important questions about the rights and obligations of doctors. Are we witnessing a sea change in the old professional values on which the NHS was built, and will medical staff of the future work to a very different 'psychological contract'? This paper opens up the debate, and argues that greater clarity about the role of professionals will be crucial to a constructive discussion about the direction of health care reform and improving the patient experience.

ISBN 185717 475 5 Autumn 2003 £6.50
Free download at: www.kingsfund.org.uk/publications

How Will Growing Pressures on Chronic Care be Managed?

How will the future NHS provide an effective response to growing demands for chronic care? Sharper market incentives – such as allowing funding to follow the patient's choice of provider, and encouraging more competition among providers, including those from the private sector – are being introduced. But these kinds of incentive seem more suitable for patients who are willing and able to travel to alternative providers for elective care, rather than patients who are old, frail and have complex chronic conditions. In the USA, managed care organisations offer excellent care for patients with chronic diseases in a competitive market. This paper asks what lessons the NHS can learn from their experience.

ISBN 185717 476 3 2003